MERRY CHRISTMAS, GOTHAM CIIIIITYYYYYY!

LEAP!

SPLOCH

MAMA, WAS THAT *SANTA?*

OKAY, NOW I'M CONFUSED.

DON'T BE. YA SEE, I'M AN *ANGEL.* WELL, NOT A *FULL* ANGEL. MORE LIKE AN ANGEL IN *TRAINING.* I HAVE SOME OF THE PERKS BUT--

STOP...

...I'VE SEEN THIS MOVIE BEFORE, AND EVEN ONE TIME AS A LIMITED FX MINISERIES WITH *TOM HARDY.* THIS AIN'T GONNA WORK ON ME.

WHEN I WATCH *IT'S A WONDERFUL LIFE,* I STOP IT RIGHT AFTER HE JUMPS. THAT WAY I HAVE SOME *RESPECT* FOR THAT SAD SACK.

THAT'S DARK.

WAIT! I DON'T DO THE *PAST* STUFF, I DO THE MULTIVERSE!

MULTIVERSE?! I THINK YA JUST BIT OFF MORE THAN YOU CAN CHEW...

PLEASE, LADY, IF I SCREW UP AGAIN, I GO BACK TO *JANITORIAL,* AND I CAN'T UNCLOG *ANOTHER* HEAVENLY DUMP.

UGH. OKAY. MAKE THIS QUICK. I GOT A MISTLETOE TAG WAITING FOR ME.

WHERE ARE WE AND WHY ARE THE DUMPSTERS SO TINY?

EARTH-42. A WORLD FULL OF LI'L--

OMG! HE'S SO SMALL!

I MAY BE SMALL, BUT I CAN STILL CRUSH YOU. GO AWAY, THIS IS MY HIDING SPOT.

WHATCHA HIDING FROM?

US!

I DON'T REMEMBAH BLACKEST NIGHT BEING THIS ADORABLE.

SO MUCH FLESH. THIS ONE WILL BE A FEAST.

NOT ON MY WATCH, BAT-MUNCH!

WHOA! I'M A GOOD GUY HERE?

I SAVE ONE PARALLEL UNIVERSE, AND SUDDENLY I'M A GOOD GUY? #%&@ YOU!

COME ON, BANE! QUIT BEING A BIG SCAREDY-CAT. THE WHITE LANTERN CORPS NEEDS YA.

IT WAS A TACTICAL RETREAT! I WILL BREAK YOUR BACK FOR THIS INSOLENCE!

YEAH, YEAH, YEAH.

NO OFFENSE, PUDDIN', BUT CHA KINDA STINK AT THIS. I MEAN, THIS WAS CUTE AND ALL... BUT I'M STILL DEPRESSED. SO WHY ARE WE HERE?

DON'T YOU SEE? YOU WENT ON TO HELP HAL JORDAN TURN THE TIDE AGAINST NEKRON... BUT I SEE YOUR POINT. THE NEXT ONE WILL BE BETTER. WATCH!

EARTH-50. GOTHAM.

THIS IS EARTH-50. HOME TO THE *JUSTICE LORDS.* BASICALLY, TYRANT VERSIONS OF HEROES ON YOUR WORLD.

I FIGHT *TYRANTS?* THAT'S STARTING TA SOUND LIKE GOOD-GUY STUFF...

...IF YA PAIR ME UP WITH THAT DORK HAL JORDAN AGAIN, IMMA KILL YOU *WITH* ME.

YOU'RE A *CRIMINAL,* I PROMISE. JUST SIT TIGHT. THE OTHER HARLEY WILL BE AROUND ANY MINUTE...

SO WHAT'S YOUR *DEAL,* ANYWAY? I DON'T EVEN KNOW YOUR *NAME.*

NO ONE HAS EVER ASKED ME THAT BEFORE. I'M *LAYMA,* BACK WHEN I WAS ALIVE, I WAS A *TRIPLET...*

...GOT SEPARATED FROM MY SIBLINGS AT BIRTH 'CAUSE THEY GOT POWERS AND I GOT *NOTHIN'.*

TRIED TO RECONNECT BUT CHICKENED OUT. RAN AWAY FROM MY PROBLEMS AND DID THE WHOLE *DIE ALONE* THING. IT'S NOT ALL IT'S CRACKED UP TO BE.

I WOUND UP IN HEAVEN CLEANING TOILETS. BEEN WORKIN' MY WAY UP TO *ANGEL* EVER SINCE.

SO YOU'RE BASICALLY FORCED TA SPEND YOUR AFTERLIFE TRYING TO SOLVE *OTHER* PEOPLE'S PROBLEMS IN AN ATTEMPT TA EMOTIONALLY SOOTHE *YOUR OWN* LOSS.

I NEVER THOUGHT ABOUT IT LIKE THAT.

YA NEED TA FIND YOUR SIBLINGS.

MAYBE YOU'RE RIGHT... WAIT A SECOND, STOP GUARDIAN-ANGELIN' ME.

POKE POKE

LOOK! THERE YOU ARE NOW. TOLD YA YOU'RE A CRIMINAL. GRAFFITI IS PUNISHABLE BY *DEATH* HERE--

HOLY #&@%, IS THAT ME AND JOKER WORKING *TOGETHER?* I THOUGHT YA WERE SUPPOSED TA CHEER ME *UP,* REMEMBER?

WHOA, IS SHE PAINTING A...

YEP!

ANYHOODLES, CAN WE PLEASE GO TO A PLACE WHERE I'M NOT TIED TO THAT @#&%?

MY BAD. LET'S TRY THIS...

EARTH-45. JOKERVILLE.

SO WHEN I SAID, *"NO JOKER,"* WHAT PART OF THAT DIDN'TCHA UNDERSTAND?

WAIT, IS THAT--?

--SY?

YA HAVE NO IDEA HOW *HAPPY* I AM TO SEE YOU!

I'VE MISSED YOU SO *MUCH!*

GET OFF ME, LADY!

MWAH

RATON

HE DOESN'T KNOW YA, 'CAUSE ON THIS EARTH YA WERE *NEVER BORN.*

I DIDN'T BRING YA HERE TO BE A JERK. THIS IS THE ONLY EARTH WHERE YOU'RE *NOT* TIED TO THE JOKER.

FEH!

WITHOUT YA, THERE WAS NOBODY TO SAVE BATMAN FROM JOKER. AND WITHOUT BATMAN, JOKER HAD NOTHING TO REBEL AGAINST. SO HE WENT...VERY *FAMILY FRIENDLY.*

I WILL SAY, HIS GLUTEN-FREE MICROWAVE CHICKEN NUGGETS ARE *DELICIOUS.*

YOU'D THINK FINDING OUT MISTAH J SOLD OUT WOULD MAKE ME FEEL *BETTAH,* BUT IT JUST KINDA BRINGS ME BACK TO WHERE I *STARTED.*

IN ALL THESE WORLDS I'VE SEEN, I'M EITHER SIDEKICKIN' OR I DON'T EXIST AT *ALL.*

SO WHAT'S THE *POINT* IF THERE AIN'T AT LEAST *ONE* WORLD WHERE *I'M* THE MOST FEARED, EVIL PERSON EVERYONE KNOWS?

FFF

YOU WANT *EVIL....?*

EARTH-33. HUNTINGTON BEACH.

I DO MY HAIR TOSS, CHECK MY NAILS. BABY, HOW YOU FEELIN'?

FEELIN' GOOD AS HELL...

HERE YA GO--THE NUMBER ONE *REALTOR* IN HUNTINGTON BEACH.

YA DON'T BELIEVE IN TIPPING, *FACEBOOK* IS YOUR PRIMARY OUTLET FOR ALL YOUR DEEP THOUGHTS...

...AND YA *ALWAYS* ASK TO SPEAK TO THE MANAGER.

UGH, I'M SO... *BASIC!*

NO! NO! NO! I CAN'T BE THIS. THIS IS *AWFUL.* THIS IS *WORSE* THAN THE WORST! *PLEASE* TAKE ME BACK HOME!

I PROMISE IF YA DO, I'LL *NEVAH* FEEL SORRY FOR MYSELF AGAIN. JUST GET ME AWAY FROM *HER.*

OKAY, OKAY!

EARTH-0. GOTHAM. CHRISTMAS EVE.

THANK YOU, LAYMA. IT'S NOW MY LIFE'S MISSION TO OUT-EVIL REALTOR HARLEY.

YOU'RE THE BEST GUARDIAN ANGEL A GAL COULD EVER HAVE. I HOPE YOU GET YOUR WINGS OR BECOME FULLY GROWN OR WHATEVER.

SMEK

I *AM* FULLY GROWN. UM... BUT THAT'S *BESIDE* THE POINT.

SEE, FOR SOME PEOPLE IT'S REMEMBERING WHO THEY *WERE,* AND FOR OTHERS, I GUESS IT'S A FEAR OF WHO THEY COULD *BECOME...*

"...HARLEY? WHERE'D YA *GO?*"

MERRY CHRISTMAS, MUGGER!

MERRY CHRISTMAS, HOMELESS SANTA!

MERRY CHRISTMAS, PERVERT!

AND MOST OF ALL...

...MERRY CHRISTMAS, *COMMISSIONER GORDON!*

BETCHA DIDN'T THINK I WAS COMING BACK. I KNOW I WASN'T MUCH IN THE *CHRISTMAS SPIRIT* BEFORE, BUT DON'T WORRY, I'M IN A *MUCH* BETTER MOOD NOW...

...THANKS TO MY *GUARDIAN ANGEL*, HE'S A *WONDER TRIPLET* OR MAYBE A *CRAZY PERSON*, I'M NOT SURE, BUT I FOUND MY JOY AGAIN BECAUSE I LEARNED THAT THE *WORLD* NEEDS ME!

AND NO MATTER HOW BAD I THINK MY LIFE IS, IT BEATS SELLING HOMES IN HUNTINGTON BEACH.

NOW WHO WANTS TO OPEN THEIR PRESENT *FIRST?*

I GOT THIS ONE FOR *YOU.*

DON'T WORRY, BABS, I GOT SOMETHING FOR YOU TOO!

DON'CHA JUST *LOVE* CHRISTMAS WITH *FAMILY?!*

THE END. HAPPY HOLIDAYS!

Victor Fries: A student of subzero thermodynamics, utilizing his scientific discoveries for malevolent means.

BIZARRO
LOVE HOLIDAY

This is Earth-23. It's just like the Earth where you live (only some things are different).

Every year, people all over the planet take part in a very special holiday known as the *Celebration of Rapport*.

One interesting fact about the Celebration of Rapport is that it started with an idea that *Superman* had.

DAVID F. WALKER
writer

GUSTAVO DUARTE
artist

MARCELO MAIOLO
colorist

WES ABBOTT
letterer

ANDREW MARINO
editor

He wanted to create a holiday that *united* the entire planet in empathy and understanding.

As you can imagine, it was difficult (creating a holiday is never easy), but because he's Superman... well...you know...he made the impossible possible.

And so, for two days out of the year, people all over the world celebrate the *same* holiday.

The-first-part-of-the holiday is known as the Day of Giving.

From the biggest cities to the smallest villages, *everyone* participates in the Day of Giving.

All over the world, people place a round crystal known as a *Self~Stone* into giant containers.

It sounds really simple (and it is), but as with many things in life, sometimes the simplest acts have the greatest meaning.

WHAT'S YOUR NAME?

I'M ASTRID!

You see, the Self~Stone represents all the hopes and fears, joys and sorrows of the person it belongs to. And every year each person gives their stone away, and gets a new one in return.

And that's how the holiday works...

...on the Day of Giving you let go of your Self~Stone, and on the Day of Receiving you get a new Self~Stone (which belonged to someone else).

For Superman, there's nothing he enjoys more than the two days that make up the Celebration of Rapport (and not just because he thought it up, but because it is something that brings people *together*).

But not everyone loves the Celebration of Rapport.

For one person, it is a reminder that no one has ever given him anything...which, when you think about it, means he's never *received* anything either.

If he had friends, they'd call him *Bizarro*, and for as far back as he can remember (which is a surprisingly long time), he has spent the Celebration of Rapport alone.

Every year, it makes Bizarro feel the same way...

HOLIDAY MAKES BIZARRO HAPPY. SO VERY HAPPY.

BIZARRO LOVE HOLIDAY! MUST DO NOTHING!

THANKS FOR HELPING OUT.

ARE YOU KIDDING...?

THE PLEASURE IS ALL MINE, GOOD SIR.

THIS IS MY FAVORITE DAY OF THE YEAR.

I MEAN, IT'S *TWO* OF MY FAVORITE DAYS.

THANK YOU FOR GIVING OF YOURSELF. THIS MEANS SO MUCH TO ME.

THANK YOU FOR GIVING OF YOURSELF.

After exchanging the Self-Stones that have been collected, Superman and the other heroes set out to prepare for the Day of Receiving.

SEE YOU TOMORROW!

WOULD THE MORROW COME WITH GREAT HASTE.

HAVE FUN!

It can be difficult for some people to understand Bizarro's hatred of the Celebration of Rapport.

But just in case you forgot...in his entire life, no one *ever* gave Bizarro a present.

Nothing for his birthday.

Nothing for Boxing Day (which is a really big holiday on Earth-23) or Arbor Day or Sinking of Atlantis Day or...

...you get the point (which is that Bizarro is seething with resentment after a lifetime of being unappreciated).

The act of giving away something that represents part of themselves, and then receiving something that represents part of a complete stranger, holds different meaning for everyone on Earth-23.

BIZARRO HAVING BAD TIME. WORST TIME EVER.

And everyone has a Celebration of Rapport that means the most to them.

But for Bizarro, his *first* Celebration of Rapport will *always* be his favorite.

NOW I KNOW YOU'RE BEING SARCASTIC, SILLY.

BIZARRO AM LYING.

BIZARRO HATE HOLIDAY!

THE END

Holo-casts are reporting record sales this last day. And traffic gridlocked from midtown to the tunnels.

It appears that everyone is out doing some last-minute holiday shopping.

While I'm out doing a search of my own.

That just happens to be located thousands of fathoms below.

Over the last few months, I've managed to access the archives on the Batcomputer when Bruce wasn't looking. And I stumbled across something interesting.

An incident report from decades ago. While trying to seal up a fissure deep beneath Gotham Harbor, an accident forced Batman to abort the mission.

His vehicle was never recovered.

The first and final voyage of the Bat-sub!

Holidays Beyond

Written by DEREK FRIDOLFS and DUSTIN NGUYEN
Art: DUSTIN NGUYEN   Colors: JOHN KALISZ
Letters: TRAVIS LANHAM   Editor: MICHAEL McCALISTER
Batman created by BOB KANE with BILL FINGER.

OW! THAT STUNG!

AT LEAST I'VE GONE SOMEWHERE NICE. THIS LOOKS LIKE METROPOLIS.

NO, TERRY. YOU'RE HOME, MANY YEARS FROM NOW.

NO SCHWAY! THIS IS GOTHAM?! IT'S...EVOLVED!

AS ALL THINGS IN TIME SHOULD. BUT SOME THINGS REMAIN THE SAME.

IF YOU'RE HERE TO DATA-BREACH AND CRED-JACK ME, YOU PICKED THE WRONG GUY.

⟨SCAN COMPLETE⟩

⟨VOICE I.D. CONFIRMED⟩

⟨McGINNIS, TERRY⟩

⟨SECURITY DISABLED⟩

⟨VAULT ACCESSED⟩

⟨ACCOUNT TRANSFER...PENDING⟩

THIS IS WHERE I TURN INTO BATMAN. I MEAN, HE WILL. HE'S... WE'RE BOTH...

JUST WATCH.

NOW THAT YOU SILICONS KNOW WHO I AM, THAT ALSO MEANS YOU KNOW--

--I'M WITH HER!

THOUGHT YOU MIGHT LIKE THIS BACK AFTER YOU CRASHED IT.

BARK BARK!

YOU'RE MISTAKEN. ALFRED WAS THE PILOT. I ONLY PULLED HIM FROM THE WRECK.

HE WOULDN'T ALLOW ME TO GO BACK FOR IT EITHER. I THINK IT EMBARRASSED HIM. FROM THAT POINT ON, HE SWORE OFF DRIVING ANYTHING BUT THE FAMILY LIMO.

SOOOO, ABOUT MY HOLIDAY BONUS...YOU FORGOT, DIDN'T YOU? I'LL ACCEPT CREDS. OR A NEW BATMOBILE. PLEASE BE A NEW *BATMOBILE*.

WHEN YOU GET TO BE MY AGE, YOU REALIZE THERE IS SOMETHING EVEN MORE VALUABLE THAN MONEY...*TIME*.

TAKE THE NIGHT OFF AND GO SPEND IT WITH DANA. OUR SEARCH FOR BLIGHT CAN BE DELAYED UNTIL TOMORROW, AFTER I REPAIR YOUR SUIT.

NO ARGUMENT HERE. I'M GONNA LEAVE BEFORE YOU CHANGE YOUR MIND.

THANK YOU FOR THE GIFT, TERRY.

THE SUB? THAT'S JUST THE WRAPPING. THE PRESENT IS INSIDE. LOOK UNDER THE SEAT.

So what do you get for the man who can buy anything?

A lost relic from his past.

END

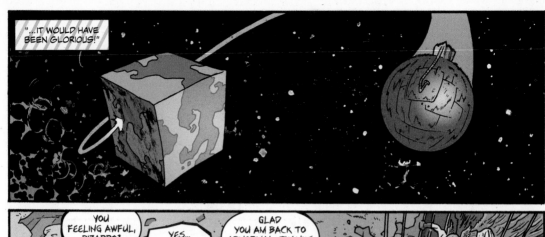

"...IT WOULD HAVE BEEN GLORIOUS!"

YOU FEELING AWFUL, BIZARRO?

YES... ME FEELING HORRIBLE NOW.

GLAD YOU AM BACK TO ABNORMAL, THANKS TO UNJUSTICE LEAGUE!

SNORRRRRR!

SQUAWK!

HEADING BACK TO GOTHTHUMB! CAN'T WAIT TO TAKE AWAY ROBZARRO'S PRESENTS!

GLAD WE SAVE YOU, BIZARRO! HELLO!

SIGH. NOW ME NEVER GET CHANCE TO TEACH THEM *TRUE* MEANING OF GIVING.

HUH. WHAT THIS?

OH! IT AM LOVELY!

YOU WELCOME! CRAPPY HOLIDAYS!

KLAANK!

HOD!

A GIFT FOR ME? MAYBE SPIRIT OF GIVING IS LOST AFTER ALL!

HAVE YOURSEL A BIZARRO LITTL CHRISTMAS!

WRITER: THOMAS E. SNIEGOSK
ARTIST: JUSTIN MASON
COLORIST: CHRIS O'HALLORAN
LETTERER: CARLOS M. MANGUAL
EDITOR: LIZ ERICKSON

A MISERABLE HOLIDAY TO ALL, AND TO ALL WAKE UP!

END.

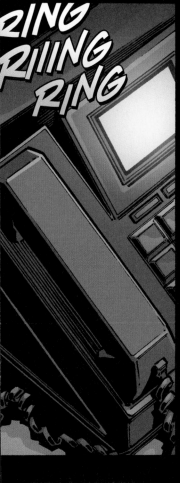

RIING RIING RING

HELLO? SLOW DOWN, SLOW DOWN, I CAN BARELY HEAR YOU...I KNOW IT'S CHRISTMAS EVE, BUT WHAT'S THE PROBLEM?

"Mhmmm. *SUPERMAN* IS WORKING HIS OTHER JOB?

"*BATMAN'S* CAR LOST A WHEEL?

"*WONDER WOMAN* IS AWAY SPENDING TIME WITH HER SISTERS?

"NOT A PROBLEM, *I'VE* GOT THIS COVERED. LOOKS LIKE A JOB FOR..."

THE END.

♪ --GONNA WALK ALL OVER YOU... ♪

THANK YOU. THANK YOU. MERRY CHRISTMAS, EVERYBODY.

LADIES AND GENTLEMEN... SPEED FREAK!

THAT WAS TERRIFIC. NICE MUSIC. NOBODY SPONTANEOUSLY COMBUSTED. JUST GREAT.

NOW, OUR NEXT GUEST IS HERE TO LIGHTEN THE MOOD. BE WARNED: IT'S GOING TO GET ZANY.

EVERYBODY PLEASE GIVE IT UP FOR THE MADCAP COMEDY OF... SHOOTING STAR!

CLAP! CLAP! CLAP!

I TOLD YOU I WANTED NO PART IN THIS.

HA HA HA HA HA HA!

WHY ARE YOU LAUGHING? THAT WASN'T A JOKE.

MY SISTER IS IN TOWN.

HA HA HA HA HA HA HA HA HA HA HA HA HA HA HA HA HA HA

PLEASE STOP.

LADIES AND GENTLEMEN, SHOOTING STAR!

SOMEBODY MUST BE ON PANDAR THE FALLEN'S NAUGHTY LIST, BUT YOU KNOW WHO ISN'T?

CLAP! CLAP! CLAP! CLAP! CLAP! CLAP!

THE GOOD FOLKS RESPONSIBLE FOR THE FOLLOWING PRODUCTS. LET'S PAUSE FOR A WORD FROM OUR SPONSORS!

TWENTY YEARS ON THE JOB AND THEY PAIR ME WITH A FRIGGING *TARP*?!

BLAM! BLAM! BLAM!

C'MON!

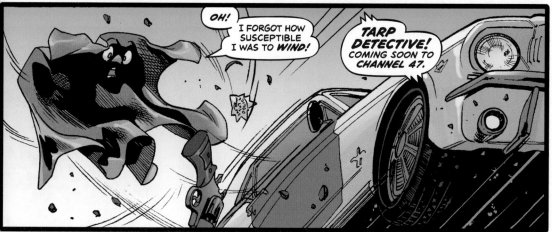

OH!

I FORGOT HOW SUSCEPTIBLE I WAS TO *WIND*!

TARP DETECTIVE! COMING SOON TO CHANNEL 47.

WELCOME BACK!

COMMERCIALS ARE GREAT. *MAGIC* IS ALSO GREAT.

HERE TO PERFORM SOME OF THE AFOREMENTIONED *MAGIC* IS OUR RESIDENT EXPERT IN ALL THINGS *PRESTIDIGITATION*, EVERYBODY PLEASE WELCOME...

MAGIC LANTERN!

OH, HEHEHE, THINK I KINDA PASSED OUT FOR A SECOND THERE. SORRY. SORRY, EVERYBODY. IT'S BEEN A LONG WEEK...

WHAT WAS I SUPPOSED TO DO AGAIN?

MAGIC.

OH YEAH, RIGHT. MAGIC. HEHE.

GOD.

MAGIC...*HEHE*... WEIRD WORD... *MAGIC*... KINDA STUPID...

WAIT. WHAT WAS I SUPPOSED TO DO AGAIN?

DO MAGIC

BOOOOO!

OKAY, OKAY DON'T *NARC* ON ME, GUYS. IT'S BEEN A LONG WEEK, OKAY?

A REALLY *LONG* WEEK.

FULL OF UPS AND DOWNS BUT YOU KNOW WHAT I ALWAYS SAY WHEN LIFE HANDS YOU--

KEEP ON TRUCKIN'

--LEMONS...?

≈YAWN...≈

I'LL BE HONEST. IF YOU DON'T LIKE THAT TRICK *YOU WON'T LIKE* ANY OF THE OTHER ONES. THEY'RE ALL JUST *SLOGANS* IN GREEN LETTERS.

YOU GUYS LIKE *MARSHALL McLUHAN* AT ALL?

THAT'S *NOT* MAGIC!

NOTHING ABOUT THIS IS FESTIVE!

JEEZ, YOU'RE JUST LIKE MY *FATHER.* IT'S *CHRISTMAS,* GUYS!

SO WHAT IF I'M A LITTLE *LESS* THAN *SOBER?*

NICE. NICE BEHAVIOR.

I HOPE YOU'RE *HAPPY.* MY *SISTER* IS SITTING THERE BY HERSELF IN MY *BACKYARD.*

DAMN YOU!

YOU DIDN'T LEAVE A *KEY* FOR HER?

THE MEDIUM IS THE MESSAGE

OKAY, LET'S ALL JUST TAKE A *BREATHER.*

DO YOU HAVE ANY IDEA HOW *DIFFICULT* IT WAS FOR MY *SISTER* TO GET HERE? THE LOGISTICS ALO--

DING DONG!

WELL, NOW *WHO* COULD THAT BE? LOOKS LIKE WE HAVE A *SPECIAL CHRISTMAS GUEST!*

IT'S *PANDAR* THE FALLEN!

YAY! IT'S PANDAR!

PANDAR'S HERE!

CLAP!

CLAP! CLAP! CLAP!

WOW! WHAT A *SURPRISE!* PANDAR, SIR. IT'S AN HONOR TO MEET YOU. JUST ONE QUESTION: HOW COME YOU DIDN'T COME DOWN THE CHIMNEY?

BUT I DID. PANDAR IS IN *EVERY* CHIMNEY.

WOW! IT'S A CHRISTMAS *MIRACLE!*

HAVE OUR OFFERINGS OF ENTERTAINMENT *SATIATED* YOU?

SILENCE.

PREZ RICKARD'S MAGICAL SCI-FI DESOLATE SOULS CLUB HOLIDAY SPECIAL

Jay Baruchel.............writer
Dominike 'Domo' Stanton
artist
Bryan Valenza................colorist
Ferran Delgado.............letterer
Andrew Marino.................editor

NICE!

Fin

A Very Lobo Hanukkah

Writer ~ TOM KING • Artist ~ SCOTT KOBLISH
Colorist ~ HI-FI • Letterer ~ ROB STEEN
Associate Editor ~ LIZ ERICKSON • Editor ~ MARIE JAVINS

LOBO THE CZARNIAN. BE WARNED.

BY ORDER OF THE **432ND HIGH COUNCIL** UNDER THE RULE OF BLESSED EMPEROR **SLAZZAKK THE BETEETHED.**

YOU HAVE BEEN **PERMANENTLY** BANNED FROM ENTERING SPACE SECTOR **3773.** THIS ORDER IS EFFECTIVE **NOW** AND IN **PERPETUITY.**

"BUT HE MOCKED THEM, AND LAUGHED AT THEM, AND ABUSED THEM SHAMEFULLY, AND SPAKE PROUDLY..."

FAILURE TO COMPLY WITH THIS ORDER WILL RESULT IN A **NUMBER** OF PREDETERMINED OUTCOMES.

FIRST, YOUR BODY WILL BE **DECIMATED** IN AS **PAINFUL** A PROCESS AS IS PERMITTED BY CIRCUMSTANCES.

SECOND, ANYONE WHO HAS EVER **KNOWN** YOU OR KNOWN **OF** YOU WILL BE HUNTED DOWN AND **EXECUTED.**

THIRD, YOUR NAME, IMAGE, AND **MEMORY** SHALL BE **ERASED** AND **CENSURED** FOR THE REMAINDER OF TIME.

"...AND SWARE IN HIS WRATH, SAYING, UNLESS JUDAS AND HIS HOST BE NOW DELIVERED INTO MY HANDS..."

DO YOU HAVE ANY QUESTIONS REGARDING THIS ORDER?

"...IF EVER I COME AGAIN IN SAFETY, I WILL BURN UP THIS HOUSE: AND WITH THAT HE WENT OUT IN A GREAT RAGE."

YEAH, Y'KNOW WHAT, I **DO** GOT A QUESTION.

I KEEP GETTING THESE **BLOODSTAIN** ON MY **HOG** FROM YO PEOPLE. I'M HAVING A **HELL OF A** TIME WITH THEM.

IS THERE, LIKE, A SPECIA **OIL** OR SOMETHI I'M SUPPOSE TO USE TO GE THEM **OUT?**

"BUT JUDAS PITCHED IN ADASA WITH THREE THOUSAND MEN, AND THERE HE PRAYED, SAYING..."

"O LORD...

"...WHEN THEY THAT WERE SENT FROM THE KING OF THE ASSYRIANS BLASPHEMED...

"...THINE ANGEL WENT OUT, AND SMOTE AN HUNDRED FOURSCORE AND FIVE THOUSAND OF THEM.

"EVEN SO DESTROY THOU THIS HOST BEFORE US THIS DAY, THAT THE REST MAY KNOW THAT HE HATH SPOKEN BLASPHEMOUSLY AGAINST THY SANCTUARY...

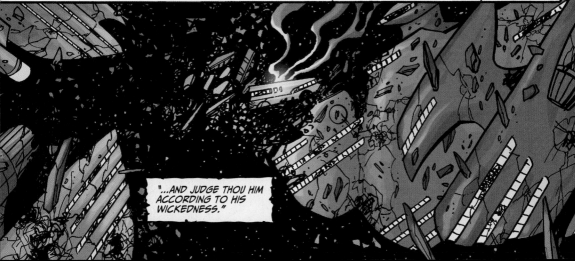

"...AND JUDGE THOU HIM ACCORDING TO HIS WICKEDNESS."

I WANT YOU TO KNOW, I'M DOING THIS FOR THE *FISH*.

I'M *NOT* HAVING FUN.

"WHEREUPON THEY CAME FORTH OUT OF ALL THE TOWNS OF JUDEA ROUND ABOUT, AND CLOSED THEM IN..."

OKAY, I'M HAVING A *LITTLE* FUN.

BUT IT'S STILL *MOSTLY* FOR THE FRAGGING FISH.

"...SO THAT THEY, TURNING BACK UPON THEM THAT PURSUED THEM, WERE ALL SLAIN WITH THE SWORD, AND NOT ONE OF THEM WAS LEFT."

AT THIS POINT, IF I *HAD* TO BE HONEST, IT'S PROBABLY *FIFTY* PERCENT FISH, *FIFTY* PERCENT FUN.

"AFTERWARDS THEY TOOK THE SPOILS, AND THE PREY, AND SMOTE OFF NICANORS HEAD, AND HIS RIGHT HAND..."

YEAH, ALL RIGHT, IT'S MOSTLY *FUN*.

BUT I'M *STILL* THINKING ABOUT THOSE *BEAUTIFUL FRAGGING FISH!*

"...WHICH HE STRETCHED OUT SO PROUDLY, AND BROUGHT THEM AWAY, AND HANGED THEM UP TOWARD JERUSALEM."

IT'S NOT *MY* FAULT. YOU BASTICHES JUST DIE *GOOD*. THAT'S ON *YOU*.

SO LET'S SAY *EIGHTY* PERCENT FUN, *TWENTY* PERCENT FISH.

THAT STILL AIN'T *BAD!*

"FOR THIS CAUSE THE PEOPLE REJOICED GREATLY..."

DAMN, THIS IS A *FRAGGING* GOOD TIME!

WHAT THE FRAG WERE WE *FIGHTING* ABOUT?

"...AND THEY KEPT THAT DAY A DAY OF GREAT GLADNESS."

IT'S THE SAME OLD *STORY*, AIN'T IT?

"WHEREUPON THERE WAS A SORE BATTLE, INSOMUCH AS MANY WERE SLAIN ON BOTH PARTS."

MY *GOD* IS BETTER THAN YOUR *GOD*.

"JUDAS ALSO WAS KILLED, AND THE REMNANT FLED."

WHAT A *FRAGGING* WASTE OF TIME.

"THEN JONATHAN AND SIMON TOOK JUDAS THEIR BROTHER, AND BURIED HIM IN THE SEPULCHRE OF HIS FATHERS IN MODIN."

WAY I SEE IT, *EVERY* PERSON GOT A RIGHT TO THEIR *OWN* GOD.

"MOREOVER THEY BEWAILED HIM, AND ALL ISRAEL MADE GREAT LAMENTATION FOR HIM, AND MOURNED MANY DAYS, SAYING..."

THAT'S WHAT MAKES *LIVING* WORTH *LIVING*.

"...HOW IS THE VALIANT MAN FALLEN, THAT DELIVERED ISRAEL!"

"AS FOR THE OTHER THINGS CONCERNING JUDAS AND HIS WARS..."

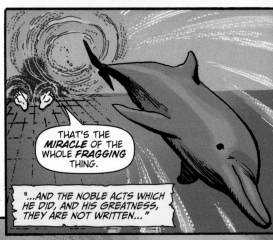

THAT'S THE *MIRACLE* OF THE WHOLE *FRAGGING* THING.

"...AND THE NOBLE ACTS WHICH HE DID, AND HIS GREATNESS, THEY ARE NOT WRITTEN..."

THERE AIN'T NO *MAIN MAN*.

"...FOR THEY WERE VERY MANY."

Y'KNOW, BESIDES *ME*.

1 Maccabees.
The King James Translation.

End